Book 7C

UNIT 1

1.1 Whole number arithmetic

Page 1 ***HWK 1M***

1. (a) 30 (b) 8000 (c) 800 (d) 5000000 **2.** (a) 48003
(b) 17024 (c) 2500 **3.** (a) 1478, 8741 (b) 3469, 9643 (c) 25689, 98652
4. eight million, one hundred and four thousand, six hundred and fifty three
5. (a) 3716 (b) 6853 (c) 492186 (d) 72296

Page 1 ***HWK 1E***

1. (a) 3219 3280 3345 3465
(b) 9018 9148 9174 9213 9306

2.

+	100	10	400	70
420	520	430	820	490
653	753	663	1053	723
199	299	209	599	269
5126	5226	5136	5526	5196

3. (a) four thousand three hundred and fifteen
(b) seventy thousand
(c) thirty-two thousand one hundred and forty
(d) six million, eight hundred and forty-two thousand, three hundred

4. (a) 1749 (b) 1580 (c) part (a) by 169
5. (a) $3 \times \boxed{100} + 6$ (b) $5 \times \boxed{1000} + 3$ (c) $4 \times \boxed{10} + \boxed{9}$
(d) $6 \times \boxed{10} + 5$ (e) $2 \times \boxed{100} + \boxed{8}$ (f) $9 \times \boxed{1000} + 4 \times \boxed{10}$

Page 2 ***HWK 2M***

1. 473 **2.** 1001 **3.** 328 **4.** 787 **5.** 263
6. 583 **7.** 7053 **8.** 3875 **9.** 9184 **10.** 2162
11. £90246 **12.** 161 **13.** 1579 **14.** 3606 **15.** 45382077

Page 2 ***HWK 2E***

1. 67, 319, $\boxed{386}$, 524, $\boxed{910}$, 42, $\boxed{952}$, 589, $\boxed{1541}$
2. 3817, 428, $\boxed{4245}$, 2317, $\boxed{6562}$, 9387, $\boxed{15949}$, 865, $\boxed{16814}$
3. 879, 5616, $\boxed{6495}$, 794, $\boxed{7289}$, 6294, $\boxed{13583}$

4. **(a)**

309 | 217 | 496 | 718
526 | 713 | 1214
1239 | 1927
3166

(b)

2318 | 643 | 82 | 728 | 4315
2961 | 725 | 810 | 5043
3686 | 1535 | 5853
5221 | 7388
12609

Page 3 ***HWK 3M***

1. 11 **2.** 34 **3.** 263 **4.** 289 **5.** 23
6. 7 **7.** 356 **8.** 537 **9.** 128 **10.** 225
11. 137 **12.** 3435 **13.** 195 **14.** £18740 **15.** 896

Page 4 ***HWK 3E***

1. 432 **2.** 1215 **3.** 138 **4.** 1172 **5.** 180
6. 241 **7.** 1558 **8.** £2447 **9.** (a) AB = 668, AC = 647
(b) AB by 21 **10.** £48100 **11.** £492 **12.** 168 **13.** 871
14. 568 **15.** 1388

Page 4 ***HWK 4M***

1. A = 8 **2.** B = 7 **3.** C = 7 **4.** D = 9 **5.** E = 6
6. F = 4 **7.** G = 3 **8.** H = 6 **9.** I = 4 **10.** J = 6
11. K = 5 **12.** L = 9 **13.** M = 2 **14.** N = 9 **15.** P = 7
16. Q = 5 **17.** R = 8 **18.** S = 8 **19.** T = 8 **20.** U = 9
21. V = 9 **22.** W = 6 **23.** Y = 4 **24.** Z = 8

25.

×	4	9	3	7	11	8	5	12	0	6
6	24	54	18	42	66	48	30	72	0	36
8	32	72	24	56	88	64	40	96	0	48
9	36	81	27	63	99	72	45	108	0	54
4	16	36	12	28	44	32	20	48	0	24
7	28	63	21	49	77	56	35	84	0	42

Page 5 ***HWK 4E***

1. (a)

×	5	7	9	4
8	40	56	72	32
6	30	42	54	24
4	20	28	36	16
9	45	63	81	36

(b)

×	4	3	8	5
11	44	33	88	55
7	28	21	56	35
9	36	27	72	45
6	24	18	48	30

(c)

×	8	3	6	9	2
4	32	12	24	36	8
6	48	18	36	54	12
7	56	21	42	63	14
5	40	15	30	45	10
9	72	27	54	81	18

(d)

×	6	7	4	5	8
9	54	63	36	45	72
3	18	21	12	15	24
8	48	56	32	40	64
4	24	28	16	20	32
7	42	49	28	35	56

Page 6 ***HWK 5M***

1. 248 **2.** 195 **3.** 344 **4.** 456 **5.** 336 **6.** 567 **7.** 190
8. 432 **9.** 1528 **10.** 3451 **11.** 4128 **12.** 1122 **13.** 2457 **14.** 3144
15. 3730 **16.** 3096 **17.** 51690 **18.** 57168 **19.** 28441 **20.** 300152

Page 6 ***HWK 5E***

1. 84 **2.** £3488 **3.** 834 **4.** £6392 **5.** 441
6. 358 × 8, larger by 2 **7.** 423 **8.** 467 **9.** 696 **10.** £8217

1.2 Short division

Page 7 ***HWK 1M***

1. 45 → 5, 72 → 8, 36 → 4, 63 → 7, 54 → 6, 81 → 9
2. 21 → 3, 49 → 7, 42 → 6, 63 → 9, 28 → 4, 56 → 8
3. 40 → 5, 64 → 8, 24 → 3, 48 → 6, 72 → 9, 56 → 7
4. 48 → 8, 24 → 4, 42 → 7, 30 → 5, 36 → 6, 54 → 9
5. (a) $49 \div \boxed{7} = 7$ (b) $36 \div \boxed{3} = 12$ (c) $\boxed{28} \div 4 = 7$
(d) $\boxed{18} \div 9 = 2$ (e) $400 \div \boxed{10} = 40$ (f) $\boxed{100} \div 5 = 20$
(g) $\boxed{72} \div 8 = 9$ (h) $63 \div \boxed{7} = 9$ (i) $\boxed{48} \div 6 = 8$
(j) $300 \div \boxed{60} = 5$ (k) $90 \div \boxed{10} = 9$ (l) $\boxed{110} \div 10 = 11$

Page 7 ***HWK 1E***

1. 36, 9, $\boxed{4}$, 7, $\boxed{28}$, 2, $\boxed{14}$, 2, $\boxed{7}$, 8, $\boxed{56}$
2. 54, 6, $\boxed{9}$, 4, $\boxed{36}$, 6, $\boxed{6}$, 4, $\boxed{24}$, 3, $\boxed{8}$, 7, $\boxed{56}$
3. 56, 8, $\boxed{7}$, 6, $\boxed{42}$, 2, $\boxed{21}$, 7, $\boxed{3}$, 10, $\boxed{30}$, 6, $\boxed{5}$, 9, $\boxed{45}$, 2, $\boxed{90}$, 9, $\boxed{10}$
4. (a) $(6 + \boxed{9}) \div 3 = 5$ (b) $(23 + \boxed{25}) \div 8 = 6$ (c) $(67 - \boxed{32}) \div 5 = 7$
(d) $(81 - \boxed{25}) \div 7 = 8$ (e) $(27 + \boxed{53}) \div 8 = 10$ (f) $(116 - \boxed{62}) \div 6 = 9$
5. 2 **6.** 64 **7.** 54

Page 8 ***HWK 2M***

1. 32 **2.** 53 **3.** 27 **4.** 24 **5.** 67 **6.** 46
7. 69 **8.** 73 **9.** 87 **10.** 49 **11.** 683 **12.** 572
13. 96 **14.** 54 **15.** 82 **16.** 659

Page 8 ***HWK 2E***

1. 638 **2.** 457 **3.** 491 **4.** 795 **5.** $8\overline{)2936}$ by 5 **6.** £763
7. 17 **8.** Yes by 15 **9.** 685 **10.** (a) 6597 (b) 89126 (c) 356849

Page 9 ***HWK 3M***

1. 39 r 3 **2.** 87 r 6 **3.** 39 r 4 **4.** 82 r 4 **5.** 57 r 6 **6.** 502 r 2
7. 1722 r 1 **8.** 1155 r 1 **9.** 2817 ÷ 7 by 1 **10.** 569 r 7 **11.** 1215 r 3 **12.** 10399 r 5
13. 5632 r 4 **14.** 448 r 4 **15.** 14593 r 3 **16.** 99530 r 3 **17.** 47195 r 4

Page 9 ***HWK 3E***

1. 4 **2.** 7 **3.** 8 **4.** 51 **5.** 28 **6.** 13
7. (a) 18 (b) 30 **8.** 71 **9.** 33 **10.** 2166

1.3 Long multiplication and division

Page 10 ***HWK 1M***

1. 832 **2.** 910 **3.** 2438 **4.** 2294 **5.** 1876 **6.** 3612
7. 3666 **8.** 4982 **9.** **(a)** £979 (b) £2611

Page 10 ***HWK 1E***

1. 8242 **2.** 9761 **3.** 28404 **4.** 33028 **5.** 32264 **6.** 52800
7. 43134 **8.** 212872 **9.** 276 **10.** Carla by £136 **11.** £27066

Page 11 ***HWK 2M***

1. 147 **2.** 42 **3.** 53 **4.** 25 **5.** 16 **6.** 51
7. 36 **8.** 63 **9.** 17 **10.** 64 **11.** 36 **12.** 89

Page 11 ***HWK 2E***

1. 17 r 13 **2.** 14 r 24 **3.** 38 r 17 **4.** 17 r 12 **5.** 17 **6.** 14, 10 left over
7. 14 **8.** (a) 36 (b) 27 (c) 67 **9.** 19, 6 extra **10.** 14, 24p left over

1.4 Using a calculator

Page 11 ***HWK 1M***

1. 2 **2.** 17 **3.** 31 **4.** 19 **5.** 54 **6.** 41
7. 11 **8.** 16 **9.** 12 **10.** 12 **11.** 1 **12.** 72

13. 19 **14.** 73 **15.** 4 **16.** (a) $5 \times \boxed{4} + 2 = 22$ (b) $\boxed{3} \times 7 - 6 = 15$

(c) $6 + 10 \div \boxed{5} = 8$ (d) $\boxed{5} + 3 \times 8 = 29$ (e) $(8 - \boxed{4}) \times 7 = 28$ (f) $15 \div (1 + \boxed{4}) = 3$

(g) $30 \div \boxed{6} + 4 = 9$ (h) $(\boxed{3} + 8) \times 6 = 66$ (i) $16 + 18 \div \boxed{2} = 25$

Page 12 ***HWK 1E***

1. 42 **2.** 14 **3.** 12 **4.** 5 **5.** 21 **6.** 0
7. 15 **8.** 31 **9.** 57 **10.** 48 **11.** 8 **12.** 70
13. 4 **14.** 81 **15.** 17 **16.** 30 **17.** 60 **18.** 8
19. 188 **20.** 41 **21.** 123

Page 12 ***HWK 2M***

1. $(4 + 3) \times 6 = 42$ **2.** $5 \times (4 - 1) = 15$ **3.** $7 + (5 \times 6) = 37$
4. $56 \div (10 - 2) = 7$ **5.** $(5 \times 4) + (2 \times 6) = 32$ **6.** $8 \times (7 - 2) - 9 = 31$
7. $(13 + 12) \div 5 = 5$ **8.** $(18 + 18 - 8) \div 4 = 7$ **9.** $4 \times (6 + 9 - 5) = 40$
10. $42 - (6 \times 6) = 6$ **11.** $15 + (6 \times 3) + 7 = 40$ **12.** $(24 - 9) \div (27 \div 9) = 5$
13. $(41 + 22) \div (3 + 6) = 7$ **14.** $(8 + 10) \times 0 + 6 = 6$ **15.** $(58 - 4) \div (48 \div 8) = 9$

Page 13 ***HWK 2E***

1. $(8 - 6) \times 3 = 6$ **2.** $(3 + 7) \times 6 = 60$ **3.** $(9 - 3) \times 5 = 30$
4. $32 \div (10 - 2) = 4$ **5.** $8 + 9 \times 4 = 44$ **6.** $10 \times (3 + 7) = 100$
7. $48 \div (12 - 4) = 6$ **8.** $64 \div (6 + 2) = 8$ **9.** $9 \times (5 + 3) = 72$
10. $28 \div (21 \div 3) = 4$ **11.** $(20 - 2) \div (5 + 1) = 3$ **12.** $(5 + 2) \times (9 - 3) = 42$

Page 13 ***HWK 3M***

1. 2.496 **2.** 7.73 **3.** 10.22 **4.** 2.16 **5.** 385.2 **6.** 11.14
7. £94.43 **8.** £13.13 **9.** Yes **10.** $2 + \frac{1.5}{0.25} = 8$, $\frac{2 + 1.5}{0.25} = 14$
11. 11.6 **12.** 15.1 **13.** 4.2 **14.** 114 **15.** 10.2 **16.** 6.2
17. 2.66 **18.** 12.34 **19.** 1.4

Page 14 ***HWK 3E***

[1] 7	4	[2] 8	6		[3] 3	1
1		1		[4] 1	4	
[5] 6	2	9	[6] 8		2	
		[7] 4	7	[8] 3	9	[9] 4
[10] 8		5		6		8
[11] 3	[12] 6		[13] 5	1	3	9
[14] 6	1	8	2			6

1.5 Sequences

Page 14 HWK 1M

1. 

2. · · · ·
· · ·

3. 7, 4 **4.** 30, 37 **5.** 4, $3\frac{1}{2}$

6. 70000, 700000 **7.** 25, 12.5 **8.** 2.6, 2.9 **9.** 19, 25

10. –6, –8 **11.** –5, –6 **12.** 56, 67 **13.** 162, 486

14. 21, 28 **15.** 88 kg

Page 15 HWK 1E

1. 13 **2.** 14 **3.** 13 **4.** –4 **5.** 16

6. 2.25 **7.** 48, 96 **8.** 400, 4000 **9.** 2.9, 2.6 **10.** 1, $\frac{1}{4}$

11. 35, 48 **12.** 405, 1215 **13.** £18300 **14.** i, k **15.** k, p

16. t, w **17.** (a) 480 (b) 45

Page 16 HWK 2M

1. (a) 9, 12, 15, 18 (b) 73, 67, 61, 55 (c) 96, 48, 24, 12 (d) 5, 10, 20, 40

2. (a) subtract 12 (b) add 0.4 (c) divide by 3 (d) subtract $\frac{1}{2}$ (e) subtract 1
(f) double **3.** 28 **4.** (a) 33 (b) 8 (c) 4, 7, 13, 25

Page 16 HWK 2E

1. (a) 8, 14, 20, 26, 32 (b) 2, 6, 18, 54, 162 (c) 80, 40, 20, 10, 5
(d) 33, 29, 25, 21, 17 (e) 3.7, 4, 4.3, 4.6, 4.9 **3.** $5 \times 99 = 495$, $6 \times 99 = 594$, $7 \times 99 = 693$

4. (a) $44444 \times 8 = 355552$, $444444 \times 8 = 3555552$ (b) 3555555552 **5.** November

1.6 Perimeter and area

Page 17 HWK 1M

1. (a) 50 cm (b) 34 cm (c) 30 cm (d) 24 cm (e) 46 cm
(f) 36 cm **2.** (a) 7.8 cm (b) 6.6 cm (c) 7.8 cm **3.** 28 cm

4. 25 cm **5.** (a) square (b) 2 cm

Page 18 HWK 1E

1. 25 m **2.** 36 cm **3.** (a) 28 cm (b) 34 cm (c) 64 cm
(d) 44 cm (e) 72 cm (f) 56 cm **4.** 10

Page 19 HWK 2M

1. (a) 24 cm^2 (b) 88 cm^2 (c) 90 cm^2 (d) 63 cm^2

2. (a) A is 9 cm^2, B is 81 cm^2 (b) 9 **3.** (a) 4 cm (b) 16 cm

4. 431 m^2 **5.** (a) 97 cm^2 (b) 60 cm^2

Page 20 ***HWK 2E***

1. 7 cm **2.** 7.5 m **3.** (a) 60 cm^2 (b) 108 cm^2 (c) 148 cm^2
(d) 133 cm^2 **4.** 32 cm **5.** 44 m^2

Page 21 ***HWK 3M***

1. A 48 cm^2, B 24 cm^2 **2.** (a) 14 cm^2 (b) 120 cm^2 (c) 27 cm^2 (d) 16 cm^2
3. 72 m^2 **4.** 3 m **5.** (a) 132 cm^2 (b) 209 cm^2 **6.** 17 cm

Page 22 ***HWK 3E***

1. (a) 126 cm^2 (b) 220 cm^2 **2.** 55 cm^2 **3.** 9 **4.** 240 m^2
5. (a) 30 m^2 (b) 16 m^2 (c) 14 m^2

Unit 2

2.1 Averages and range

Page 23 ***HWK 1M***

1. (a) mean = 6 (b) median = 7 (c) mode = 9 (d) range = 7
2. (a) mean = 114 (b) median = 112 (c) mode = 120 (d) range = 12
3. (a) mean = 14 (b) median = 14 (c) mode = 15 (d) range = 8
4. (a) mean = 5 (b) median = 4.5 (c) mode = 3 (d) range = 8
5. 42 kg **6.** 5 **7.** Kyle by 52

Page 23 ***HWK 1E***

1. (a) 5 (b) 7 (c) 5.8 **2.** True **3.** No **4.** 6, 10
5. 4 **6.** (a) impossible (b) possible (c) true (d) impossible
7. (a) 10 (b) 12

Page 24 ***HWK 2M***

1. (a) median = 3, range = 7 (b) median = 5, range = 12
(c) 'The median for Year 7 is smaller than the median for Year 10 and the range for Year 7 is smaller than the range for Year 10 (the results for Year 7 are less spread out).'
2. (a) mean = 2.5, range = 4 (b) mean = 3, range = 5

2.2 Fractions

Page 25 ***HWK 1M***

1. (a) $\frac{7}{10} = \frac{\boxed{14}}{20}$ (b) $\frac{2}{5} = \frac{\boxed{16}}{40}$ (c) $\frac{5}{8} = \frac{\boxed{15}}{24}$ (d) $\frac{1}{7} = \frac{\boxed{5}}{35}$ (e) $\frac{8}{9} = \frac{24}{\boxed{27}}$ (f) $\frac{3}{8} = \frac{27}{\boxed{72}}$
(g) $\frac{5}{6} = \frac{\boxed{40}}{48}$ (h) $\frac{2}{11} = \frac{8}{\boxed{44}}$ (i) $\frac{7}{20} = \frac{21}{\boxed{60}}$ (j) $\frac{9}{100} = \frac{36}{\boxed{400}}$ (k) $\frac{16}{25} = \frac{\boxed{48}}{75}$ (l) $\frac{7}{15} = \frac{\boxed{35}}{75}$
2. (a) $\frac{2}{5}$ (b) $\frac{2}{3}$ (c) $\frac{3}{7}$ (d) $\frac{3}{5}$ (e) $\frac{1}{3}$ (f) $\frac{4}{5}$
(g) $\frac{7}{9}$ (h) $\frac{6}{19}$ (i) $\frac{3}{4}$ (j) $\frac{3}{5}$ **3.** $\frac{10}{15}, \frac{18}{27}, \frac{30}{45}, \frac{24}{36}$

Page 26 ***HWK 1E***

1. (a) $\frac{7}{12} = \frac{\boxed{14}}{24} = \frac{21}{\boxed{36}}$ (b) $\frac{7}{9} = \frac{\boxed{42}}{54} = \frac{49}{\boxed{63}}$ (c) $\frac{\boxed{1}}{3} = \frac{6}{18} = \frac{\boxed{5}}{15}$ (d) $\frac{3}{24} = \frac{\boxed{4}}{32} = \frac{\boxed{1}}{8}$
2. I HAVE FINISHED MY HOMEWORK

Page 26 ***HWK 2M***

1. (a) 7 (b) 5 (c) 9 (d) 8 **2.** (a) £9 (b) 9 cm (c) 9 kg
(d) 20 kg (e) £5 (f) 15g (g) 12 cm (h) £80 (i) 25 kg

3. (a) 6 (b) 7 (c) 10 (d) 20 (e) 3 (f) 30

4. (a) 7 (b) 49 **5.** 198 cm

Page 27 HWK 2E

1. (a) 4 (b) 20 (c) 8 (d) 21 (e) 30 (f) 24 (g) 6 (h) 144 **2.** £2 **3.** 80 **4.** $\frac{6}{7}$ of 42 **5.** (a) 200 kg (b) 60 cm (c) £105 (d) £66 (e) 49 litres (f) 1170 kg (g) 64 g (h) £84 (i) £117 **6.** 104

Page 28 HWK 3M

1. $\frac{1}{5}+\frac{2}{5}=\frac{\boxed{3}}{5}$ **2.** $\frac{\boxed{2}}{8}+\frac{3}{8}=\frac{\boxed{5}}{8}$ **3.** $\frac{4}{7}$ **4.** $\frac{7}{9}$ **5.** $\frac{5}{8}$ **6.** $\frac{3}{20}$

7. $\frac{15}{16}$ **8.** $\frac{8}{18}=\frac{4}{9}$ **9.** $\frac{3}{20}$ **10.** $\frac{22}{25}$ **11.** $\frac{3}{8}$ kg **12.** $\frac{7}{10}$

Page 28 HWK 3E

1. (a) $\frac{\boxed{4}}{12}+\frac{\boxed{3}}{12}=\frac{\boxed{7}}{12}$ (b) $\frac{\boxed{12}}{20}-\frac{\boxed{5}}{20}=\frac{\boxed{7}}{20}$ (c) $\frac{\boxed{63}}{70}-\frac{\boxed{30}}{70}=\frac{\boxed{33}}{70}$ **2.** $\frac{11}{15}$ **3.** $\frac{11}{28}$

4. $\frac{5}{12}$ **5.** $\frac{13}{30}$ **6.** $\frac{41}{63}$ **7.** $\frac{8}{99}$ **8.** $\frac{3}{40}$ **9.** $\frac{28}{60}=\frac{7}{15}$ **10.** $\frac{43}{180}$

11. $\frac{77}{80}$ **12.** $\frac{5}{20}=\frac{1}{4}$ **13.** $\frac{23}{70}$ **14.** (a) $\frac{19}{30}$ (b) $\frac{11}{30}$ **15.** $\frac{79}{120}$ cm **16.** $\frac{19}{60}$

2.3 Fractions, decimals, percentages

Page 29 HWK 1M

1. (a) 0.3 (b) 0.17 (c) 0.25 (d) 0.43 (e) 0.1 **2.** (a) 0.12 (b) 0.95 (c) 0.8 (d) 0.9 (e) 0.75 (f) 0.65 (g) 0.5 (h) 0.76 (i) 0.3 (j) 0.55 **3.** (a) $\frac{9}{25}$ (b) 0.36

Page 29 HWK 1E

1. (a) 0.7 (b) 0.024 (c) 0.25 (d) 0.076 (e) 0.75 (f) 0.12 (g) 0.126 (h) 0.312 (i) 0.021 (j) 0.8 **2.** 0.9 **3.** 0.65

4.

$\frac{1}{25}$	$\frac{3}{20}$	$\frac{4}{5}$	$\frac{17}{1000}$	$\frac{3}{4}$	$\frac{19}{50}$	$\frac{13}{52}$	$\frac{1}{50}$	$\frac{45}{500}$
0.04	0.15	0.8	0.017	0.75	0.38	0.25	0.02	0.09

Page 30 HWK 2M

1. (a) $\frac{9}{10}$ (b) $\frac{3}{100}$ (c) $\frac{29}{100}$ (d) $\frac{1}{2}$ (e) $\frac{87}{100}$ (f) $\frac{63}{100}$ (g) $\frac{3}{4}$ (h) $7\frac{9}{10}$ (i) $3\frac{83}{100}$ (j) $4\frac{17}{100}$ **2.** (a) $\frac{43}{100}$ (b) $\frac{57}{100}$

3. (a) $\frac{8}{10}=\frac{4}{5}$ (b) $\frac{6}{100}=\frac{3}{50}$ (c) $\frac{36}{100}=\frac{9}{25}$ (d) $\frac{87}{100}$ (e) $\frac{18}{100}=\frac{9}{50}$ (f) $\frac{35}{100}=\frac{7}{20}$

Page 30 ***HWK 2E***

1. (a) $\frac{3}{5}$ (b) $\frac{2}{25}$ (c) $\frac{7}{25}$ (d) $\frac{9}{20}$ (e) $\frac{17}{50}$ (f) $\frac{13}{20}$
(g) $\frac{1}{4}$ (h) $\frac{7}{50}$ (i) $\frac{1}{5}$ (j) $\frac{19}{25}$ (k) $5\frac{2}{5}$ (l) $3\frac{6}{25}$
(m) $5\frac{17}{20}$ (n) $8\frac{3}{4}$ (o) $2\frac{4}{25}$ **2.** $\frac{14}{25}$ **3.** A – J, B – I, C – F, D – G, E – H

Page 31 ***HWK 3M***

1. (a) $\frac{9}{10}$ (b) $\frac{23}{50}$ (c) $\frac{13}{100}$ (d) $\frac{3}{50}$ (e) $\frac{9}{20}$ **2.** (a) 35%
(b) $\frac{34}{100} = 34\%$ (c) $\frac{60}{100} = 60\%$ (d) $\frac{48}{100} = 48\%$ **3.** Gary **4.** 45% **5.** $\frac{3}{10}, \frac{1}{3}, \frac{9}{25}, \frac{2}{5}, \frac{9}{20}, \frac{23}{50}, \frac{1}{2}$

Page 32 ***HWK 3E***

1. (a) 0.39 (b) 0.38 (c) 0.2 (d) 0.29 (e) 1.4 (f) 3.75
2. (a) $\frac{61}{100} = 61\%$ (b) $\frac{60}{100} = 60\%$ (c) $\frac{9}{100} = 9\%$ (d) $\frac{16}{100} = 16\%$
3. Lee **4.** $\frac{7}{50}$ **5.**

$\frac{13}{25}$	$\frac{3}{20}$	$\frac{19}{100}$	$\frac{6}{25}$	$\frac{13}{50}$	$\frac{13}{20}$	$\frac{9}{50}$	$\frac{23}{25}$
0.52	0.15	0.19	0.24	0.26	0.65	0.18	0.92
52%	15%	19%	24%	26%	65%	18%	92%

2.4 Angles

Page 32 ***HWK 1M***

1. $P\hat{R}Q$ or $Q\hat{R}P$ **2.** $X\hat{W}Z$ or $Z\hat{W}X$ **3.** $B\hat{A}E$ or $E\hat{A}B$ **4.** (a) 77° (b) 64°
5. (a) 42° (b) 53° (c) 93° (d) 112° **6.** (a) 58° (b) 122°

Page 33 ***HWK 1E***

1. $a = R\hat{Q}T$, $b = Q\hat{T}R$, $c = R\hat{S}T$, $d = Q\hat{P}T$, $e = Q\hat{R}T$, $f = R\hat{T}S$, $g = P\hat{Q}T$
2. $p = A\hat{B}C$, $q = A\hat{F}G$, $r = D\hat{A}E$, $s = A\hat{D}E$, $t = A\hat{C}B$, $u = A\hat{G}F$
3. (a) 32° (b) 30° (c) 65° (d) 97° (e) 105° (f) 86°
(g) 87° (h) 62° (i) 132° (j) 100° (k) 127° (l) 112°

Page 34 ***HWK 2M***

1. (a) 55° (b) 42° (c) 26° (d) 50° (e) 108° (f) 75°
(g) 72° (h) 30° (i) 63° (j) 105° (k) 100° (l) 44°

Page 35 ***HWK 3M***

Allow all angles ±5° for the estimate.

1. 90° **2.** 50° **3.** 35° **4.** 125° **5.** 150° **6.** 75°

7. 310° **8.** 140° **9.** (a) 40° (b) 40° (c) 110° (d) 105°
10. (a) 90° (b) 120° (c) 55° (d) 35°

Page 35 ***HWK 3E***

1. right angle **2.** acute **3.** acute **4.** obtuse **5.** obtuse **6.** acute
7. reflex **8.** obtuse **9.** (a) acute (b) acute (c) obtuse (d) acute
10. (a) right angle (b) obtuse (c) acute (d) acute

Page 36 ***HWK 4M***

1. $a = 25°$ **2.** $b = 117°$ **3.** $c = 36°$ **4.** $d = 49°$ **5.** $e = 56°$ **6.** $f = 116°, g = 64°$
7. $h = 71°$ **8.** $i = 38°$

Page 36 ***HWK 4E***

1. $a = 35°$ **2.** $b = 67°$ **3.** $c = 48°$ **4.** $d = 95°$ **5.** $e = 100°$ **6** $f = 20°, 2f = 40°, 6f = 120°$
7. $g = 19°, 2g = 38°, 3g = 57°$ **8.** $2h = 46°, 3h = 69°, 4h = 92°$

Page 37 ***HWK 5M***

1. a = 69° **2.** $b = 62°$ **3.** $c = 47°$ **4.** $d = 69°, e = 69°$ **5.** $f = 70°, g = 44°$
6. $h = 41°, i = 82°$ **7.** $j = 74°, k = 77°, l = 103°$ **8.** $m = 66°, n = 66°$ **9.** 7°

Page 38 ***HWK 5E***

1. $a = 37°$ **2.** $b = 68°, c = 44°$ **3.** $d = 60°, e = 120°$ **4.** $f = 54°, g = 72°, h = 72°$
5. $i = 67°, j = 67°$ **6.** $k = 78°, l = 51°$ **7.** $m = 62°, n = 56°$ **8.** $p = 116°$ **9.** 59° **10.** 4°

2.5 Rules of Algebra

Page 38 ***HWK 1M***

1. $x - 13$ **2.** $4y$ **3.** $2m + 6$ **4.** $5p - 3$ **5.** $9w + 15$ **6.** $\frac{B}{4}$
7. $7A - 2$ **8.** $\frac{Y}{10} + 3$ **9.** $m + 3 + n + p$ **10.** $b + c$ **11.** $x - 9$ **12.** $n + 16$

Page 39 ***HWK 1E***

1. $3x - y$ **2.** $2m + p$ **3.** $q - r + 5$ **4.** $2a + 7 + b$ **5.** $6n + 3p - 4q$
6. $4w - y + 7p$ **7.** $3f + 2g + 6h - 9$ **8.** $4a - 8b - 3c$ **9.** $38 - x$ **10.** $y - 5$
11. $2w$ **12.** $89 + x - m$ **13.** $3n + 6$ **14.** $4w - 5$

Page 40 ***HWK 2M***

1. $8b$ **2.** $4x$ **3.** $9a - 4b$ **4.** $6m$ **5.** $10a$ **6.** $4h$ **7.** y
8. $4x + 7$ **9.** $8m + 1$ **10.** $17x$ **11.** $9p - 5$ **12.** $14y$ **13.** $5b$ **14.** $34m$
15. $18a$ **16.** $19a - 3$ **17.** $9n$ **18.** $25n + 14$ **19.** $5y + 2$ **20.** $28q$

Page 40 ***HWK 2E***

1. $8m + 9n$ **2.** $8p + 16q$ **3.** $4a + 9b$ **4.** $2x + 3y$ **5.** $22f + 7g$ **6.** $8m + 3$
7. $7b + 2c$ **8.** $7m + 1$ **9.** $27 + y$ **10.** $7x + 5y$ **11.** $2a + 30$ **12.** $4 + 7n$
13. $9w + 15$ **14.** $2p + 19$ **15.** $25 + 12m$
16. $3a$, $5b$, $\boxed{3a + 5b}$, $7b$, $\boxed{3a + 12b}$, $2a$, $\boxed{a + 12b}$, $9a$, $\boxed{10a + 12b}$
17. $7m$, 9, $\boxed{7m + 9}$, 16, $\boxed{7m + 25}$, $5m$, $\boxed{12m + 25}$, $10m$, $\boxed{2m + 25}$, 25, $\boxed{2m}$
18. $3x$, $6y$, $\boxed{3x + 6y}$, $2x$, $\boxed{x + 6y}$, $8x$, $\boxed{9x + 6y}$, $4y$, $\boxed{9x + 2y}$, $9x$, $\boxed{2y}$
19. $3m - 4n$ **20.** $-12x - 5y$

Page 41 ***HWK 3M***

1. $3 \times n$, $n + n + n$, $4n - n$, $2n + n$, $n \times 3$ **2.** (a) $4n + n = 5 \times n$, $n + n = 7n - 5n$
3. (a) $3a + 3b - a$, $2a + 2b + b$, $6a + b - 4a + 2b$, $a + 4b - b + a$ (b) should all be equal to 22

Page 41 ***HWK 3E***

1. true **2.** true **3.** true **4.** true **5.** false **6.** false
7. true **8.** false **9.** false **10.** true **11.** false **12.** false
13. false **14.** true **15.** false **16.** $n + p$ **17.** $(a + 6b)$ metres

Page 42 ***HWK 4M***

1. $p = 24$ **2.** $p = 20$ **3.** (a) $A = 36$ (b) $A = 92$ (c) $A = 228$ **4.** $p = 57$
5. $p = 76$ **6.** (a) $A = 29$ (b) $A = 239$ (c) $A = 722$

Page 42 ***HWK 4E***

1. $m = 21$ **2.** $b = 11$ **3.** $a = 7$ **4.** $w = 13$ **5.** $f = 7$ **6.** $y = 45$
7. $a = 36$ **8.** $k = 21$ **9.** $p = 63$ **10.** $y = 165$ **11.** $m = 96$ **12.** $a = 144$
13. $d = 1$ **14.** $v = 104$ **15.** $y = 33$ **16.** $m = 372$

Page 43 ***HWK 5M***

1. 9 **2.** 45 **3.** 8 **4.** 30 **5.** 12 **6.** 9
7. 45 **8.** 10 **9.** 9

Page 44 ***HWK 5E***

1. ⌒ = 9, ▽ = 9 **2.** ⌒ = 7, ☆ = 14 **3.** ▽ = 6, ⌒ = 12 **4.** ▽ = 5, ☆ = 5
5. ☆ = 3, ⌒ = 6 **6.** ⌒ = 0, ☆ = 16 **7.** ☆ = 7, ▽ = 7 **8.** ☆ = 6, ▽ = 12
9. ☆ = 10, ⌒ = 20 **10.** ⌒ = 45, ▽ = 15

Unit 3

3.1 Coordinates

Page 45 ***HWK 1M***

1. HOGWARTS **2.** (a) (2, 6) (b) (3, 4) (c) 3 ways (d) (1, 0) (e) (7, 2) (f) (6, 5) (g) 4 ways

Page 45 ***HWK 1E***

1. What do you call a man with a spade in his head? Doug
2. What do you call a dead parrot? Polygon
3. With what do you stuff a dead parrot? Polyfilla

Page 47 ***HWK 2M***

1. umbrella **2.** dog **3.** boat

Page 47 ***HWK 2E***

1. (5, 2) **2.** (3, 6) **3.** (a) (5, 1) (b) (3.5, 2.5) **4.** (b) (7, 4)
5. (a) (9, 1) (b) (5, 7) (c) (4, 8) **6.** (4, 5)

3.2 Long multiplication and division 2

Page 49 ***HWK 1M***

1. (a) 1702 (b) 4761 (c) 11900 (d) 15996 **2.** (a) 53 (b) 26 (c) 36
3. 962 **4.** 391 **5.** (a) 54 (b) 28 **6.** B **7.** £57

Page 49 ***HWK 1E***

1. 21 r 11 **2.** 21 r 15 **3.** 6664 **4.** 18 r 25 **5.** 8928 **6.** 16 r 25
7. 14 **8.** 13 **9.** 75 **10.** £924 **11.** 18 **12.** 1215

3.3 Decimals 1

Page 50 ***HWK 1M***

1. $a = 0.4$, $b = 0.7$, $c = 1.3$, $d = 2.7$, $e = 3.6$, $f = 3.9$ **2.** (a) 0.8 (b) 2.2 (c) 0.9 (d) 2.6 (e) 2.8 (f) 1.6 (g) 2.4 (h) 1.9
3. (a) 4.5 kg (b) 0.5 kg **4.** (a) 1.5, 1.7, 1.9 (b) 2, 2.6, 3.2 (c) 1.2, 0.9, 0.6
5. (a) $\frac{3}{100}$ (b) $\frac{4}{10}$ (c) $\frac{3}{10}$ (d) 40 (e) $\frac{6}{100}$

Page 50 ***HWK 1E***

1. $\frac{4}{10}$, $\frac{2}{100}$, $\frac{7}{1000}$ **2.** 0.09 **3.** 0.17 **4.** (a) 0.62 (b) 0.533 (c) 0.82 (d) 0.9 (e) 5.7 (f) 0.8 (g) $\frac{7}{10}$ (h) neither (i) 3.3 (j) 0.7 **5.** (a) 0.2 (b) 0.2 (c) 0.006 (d) 0.3 **6.** 0.3 kg

Page 51 ***HWK 2M***

1. (a) 0.28, 0.33, 0.48 (b) 0.19, 0.2, 0.34 (c) 0.03, 0.1, 0.12
(d) 0.903, 0.92, 0.925 (e) 0.62, 0.68, 0.7, 0.73 (f) 9.2, 9.31, 9.36, 9.399
(g) 0.08, 0.24, 0.307, 0.4 (h) 0.4, 0.501, 0.52, 0.53
2. 9.42 **3.** 7.288 **4.** (a) Tom (b) Tom, Carl, Dan, Matt, Alex, Sunil

Page 51 ***HWK 2E***

1. 0.4 **2.** 3.8 **3.** 1.7 **4.** 7.6 **5.** 2.03 **6.** 0.04
7. 48 **8.** 0.43 **9.** 3.25 **10.** 2.25 **11.** 62.5 **12.** 4.45
13. 7.8 **14.** 6.45 **15.** 17.6

Page 52 ***HWK 3M***

1. 13.63 **2.** 20.6 **3.** 2.8 **4.** 1.7 **5.** 13.47 **6.** 9.79
7. 1.3 **8.** 2.2 **9.** 7.44 **10.** 25.42 **11.** 4.7 **12.** 3.24
13. 13.18 **14.** (a) 1.45 (b) 10.13 (c) 1.73 (d) 8.18

Page 52 ***HWK 3E***

1. 61 p **2.** £6.63 **3.** £5.79 **4.** Alonso by 16 p **5.** (a) No (b) £8.81
6. (a) 0.043 (b) 5.741 (c) 9.738 (d) 14.246 **7.** £1.95

3.4 Multiplying and dividing by decimals

Page 53 ***HWK 1M***

1. (a) 524 (b) 79.3 (c) 8.6 (d) 1.9 (e) 640 (f) 6174
(g) 3400 (h) 3600 **2.** (a) 0.691 (b) 13.48 (c) 4.35 (d) 0.024
(e) 0.058 (f) 0.817 (g) 5.96 (h) 0.028 **3.** (a) 100 (b) 3.2
(c) 9.46 (d) 1000 (e) 0.144 (f) 10 (g) 100 (h) 8
(i) 571 **4.** £230

Page 53 ***HWK 1E***

1. 6.2, 620, 6200, 62 **2.** 0.8, 80, 8, 800 **3.** 37, 3.7, 370, 37
4. 483, 4.83, 48.3, 4830 **5.** 8.9, 890, 89, 0.89 **6.** 20, 2, 20, 0.2
7. 6.1, 610, 0.61, 6.1 **8.** 0.834, 834, 83.4, 8340 **9.** 93, 9300, 930, 9.3
10. 11.9, 1.19, 119, 0.119 **11.** £3.80 **12.** 254 m

Page 54 ***HWK 2M***

1. 16.2 **2.** 0.42 **3.** 24.05 **4.** 4.24 **5.** 110.7 **6.** 13.84
7. 2.85 **8.** 103.2 **9.** £43.25 **10.** £78.80 **11.** (a) 5 (b) 0.6
(c) 3 (d) 0.03

Page 54 ***HWK 2E***

1. £11.04 **2.** 4.23 kg **3.** 11 pounds **4.** £4.92 **5.** £1.98
6. (a) 2.3, 13.8, 1.38, 5.52 (b) 0.9, 7.2, 720, 120 (c) 0.07, 0.28, 2.8, 1.4 **7.** £573

Page 55 ***HWK 3M***

1. 3.1 **2.** 7.6 **3.** 1.9 **4.** 3.8 **5.** 21.6 **6.** 4.28
7. 5.19 **8.** 12.8 **9.** 8.28 **10.** 32.3 **11.** 21.64 **12.** 8.89
13. 15.1 **14.** 6.32 **15.** 417.9

Page 55 ***HWK 3E***

1. £68.25 **2.** £28.60 **3.** 6.4 kg **4.** 2.14 litres **5.** (a) 2.75 (b) 3.225
(c) 5.45 (d) 6.184 (e) 8.25 (f) 16.25 (g) 28.3 (h) 0.032
6. 51.6 kg **7.** £18.72

3.5 Properties of numbers

Page 55 ***HWK 1M/1E***

1. 7, 13, 19 **2.** 7, 11 **3.** e.g. $7 - 5 = 2$, $5 - 3 = 2$, $13 - 11 = 2$, **4.** 31, 37
5. $2 + 3 + 5 + 7 = 17$ **6.** Yes **7.** (a) 101, 103, 107, 109

Page 56 ***HWK 2M***

1. 9 **2.** 1, 2, 4, 7, 14, 28 **3.** (a) 1, 2, 4, 8 (b) 1, 2, 11, 22 (c) 1, 2, 3, 5, 6, 10, 15, 30
4. 25 **5.** 1, 3 **6.** (a) 1, 7 (b) 1, 13 (c) 1, 5 (d) 1, 17 **7.** 2

Page 56 ***HWK 2E***

1. (b) $40 = 2 \times 2 \times 2 \times 5$ **2.** (b) $48 = 2 \times 2 \times 2 \times 2 \times 3$ **3.** (a) $2 \times 2 \times 2 \times 3 \times 5$
(b) $2 \times 2 \times 3 \times 5 \times 5$ (c) $2 \times 5 \times 5 \times 7$ (d) 5×13 **4.** Two

Page 57 ***HWK 3M***

1. 8 **2.** 9 **3.** (a) 6, 12, 18, 24, 30 (d) 9, 18, 27, 36, 45 (c) 30, 60, 90, 120, 150
4. 70, 80 **5.** 28, 63, 84 **6.** eg. 20, 40, 60 **7.** eg. 24, 48 **8.** 93

Page 57 ***HWK 3E***

1. 6 **2.** (a) 1, 2, 4, 5, 10, 20 (b) 1, 2, 3, 5, 6, 10, 15, 30 (c) 10
3. (a) 12 (b) 5 **4.** 36 **5.** (a) 6, 12, 18, 24, 30, 36 (b) 8, 16, 24, 32, 40, 48
(c) 24 **6.** (a) 36 (b) 60 **7.** 4 and 5

Page 58 ***HWK 4M***

1. 49 **2.** 81 **3.** 121 **4.** 34 **5.** 64 **6.** 28

7. 37 **8.** 208 **9.** 300 **10.** 36 **11.** (a) $5 \times 5 = 4 \times 4 + 9$, $6 \times 6 = 5 \times 5 + 11$,
$7 \times 7 = 6 \times 6 + 13$, $8 \times 8 = 7 \times 7 + 15$, $9 \times 9 = 8 \times 8 + 17$, $10 \times 10 = 9 \times 9 + 19$
(b) $14 \times 14 + 29$ (c) $19 \times 19 + 39$ **12.** true

Page 58 ***HWK 4E***

1. (a) 9 (b) 12 (c) 15 **2.** (a) 16 + 64 (b) 9 + 81 (c) 64 + 100
(d) 49 + 121 **3.** 20, 36, 81 **4.** (a) 100 – 49 (b) 64 – 9 (c) 81 – 4 (d) 121 – 25
5. (a) 46 (b) 28 (c) 32 (d) 83 **6.** 4 + 16 + 49 + 100

3.6 Straight line graphs

Page 59 ***HWK 1M***

1. C: $x = 2$, D: $x = 7$, E: $y = -2$, F: $y = 5$, G: $x = -3$ **2.** (5, 1)
3. (a) V, Q, T (b) $x = 6$ (c) P, V, U (d) S

Page 60 ***HWK 1E***

1. (a) (0, 3), (1, 4), (2, 5), (3, 6), (4, 7), (5, 8) $y = x + 3$
(b) (0, 5), (1, 4), (2, 3), (3, 2), (4, 1), (5, 0) $x + y = 5$
2. $y = 2x$ **3.** $y = x - 6$ **4.** (a) $y = x$ (b) $x = 6$ (c) $x + y = 8$
(d) $y = x + 2$ (e) $x + y = 10$

Page 61 ***HWK 2M***

1. (a) 3 (b) 5 (c) 6 **2.** (a) 18 (b) 42 (c) 72
3. yes **4.** $y = 4x$ **5.** P: $y = 3 - x$, Q: $y = x - 1$ **6.** (a) 9 (b) 11
(c) 41 **7.** B, C

Page 62 ***HWK 2E***

1. (a) 10 (b) 11 (c) 12 (d) (3, 10) (4, 11) (5, 12) **2.** (1, 3) (2, 4) (3, 5) (4, 6)
3. (2, –1), (3, 0), (4, 1) **4.** (0, 5), (1, 4), (2, 3), (3, 2) **5.** (2, 3) (3, 5) (4, 7) (5, 9)

3.7 Handling data

Page 62 ***HWK 1M***

1. (a) 10 (b) 9 (c) 22 (d) 3 (e) 38 **2.** (a) 10, 6, 12, 4
3. (a) E (b) U (c) 50 (d) 25 (e) I

Page 63 ***HWK 1E***

1. (a) 2, 3, 5, 7, 6, 4, 4, 1

Page 64 ***HWK 2M***

1. (a) 6 (b) 9 (c) 25 (d) 10 **2.** (a) 7, 4, 6, 4, 3 (c) 10

Page 65 ***HWK 2E***

1. (a) 11 (b) May and October (c) November – heavy rain (d) 12
3. (a) 20°C (b) 12°C (c) 18°C (d) 12:00 and 18:00 (e) 09:00
(f) 09:30 and 19:00 (g) 16:00

Page 66 ***HWK 3M***

1. (a) $\frac{1}{6}$ (b) $\frac{1}{3}$ (c) England = 100, Scotland = 50, Wales = 150
2. (a) $\frac{1}{8}$ (b) 7, 14, 7, 28 (c) 45° **3.** (a) $\frac{1}{8}$ (b) $\frac{3}{8}$ (c) 18 (d) 27

Page 67 ***HWK 3E***

2. (a) Anna not correct (b) Harry is correct **3.** (a) Marie is correct (b) more men

3.8 Probability 1

Page 68 ***HWK 1M***

1. (A), (B), (D) are correctly placed and (F) is correctly placed assuming the scriptwriters are on Doctor Who's side!

Page 69 ***HWK 3M***

1. (a) $\frac{1}{8}$ (b) $\frac{1}{8}$ (c) $\frac{1}{2}$ (d) $\frac{1}{4}$ (e) $\frac{1}{2}$ **2.** (a) $\frac{1}{6}$ (b) $\frac{1}{3}$ (c) $\frac{1}{3}$
3. (a) $\frac{1}{6}$ (b) $\frac{3}{8}$ (c) $\frac{2}{5}$ (d) $\frac{7}{10}$ **4.** (a) $\frac{1}{7}$ (b) $\frac{4}{7}$ (c) $\frac{2}{7}$

Page 70 ***HWK 3E***

1. (a) $\frac{1}{4}$ (b) $\frac{1}{4}$ **2.** $\frac{1}{8}$ **3.** $\frac{1}{3}$ **4.** (a) $\frac{3}{10}$ (b) $\frac{1}{2}$ (c) $\frac{1}{5}$
5. (a) $\frac{1}{6}$ (b) $\frac{1}{6}$ (c) $\frac{1}{2}$ **6.** (a) $\frac{3}{20}$ (b) $\frac{1}{2}$ (c) $\frac{1}{4}$ (d) $\frac{1}{10}$
(e) $\frac{13}{20}$ (f) 0 **7.** (a) $\frac{12}{25}$ (b) $\frac{8}{25}$ (c) $\frac{17}{25}$ (d) 1

3.9 Applying mathematics in a range of contexts

Page 71 ***HWK 1M/2M/3M/4M/5M***

1. 15 **2.** 76 minutes **3.** 9 cm^2 **4.** 6 **5.** £1.14 **6.** 133
7.

3	6	10	15
16	9	5	4
13	12	8	1
2	7	11	14

8. rhombus **9.** 20° **10.** 28 days

UNIT 4

4.1 Constructing triangles

Page 73 ***HWK 1M***

5. about 11 cm

Page 74 ***HWK 1E***

1. 6.2 cm **2.** 4 cm **3.** 8.4 cm **4.** 115° **5.** AB = 3.5 cm, AD = 5.9 cm

4.2 Two dimensional shapes

Page 74 ***HWK 1M/1E***

1. true **2.** false **3.** (a) CD and EF (b) BC and DE

4. (a) two (b) none **5.** (c) perpendicular

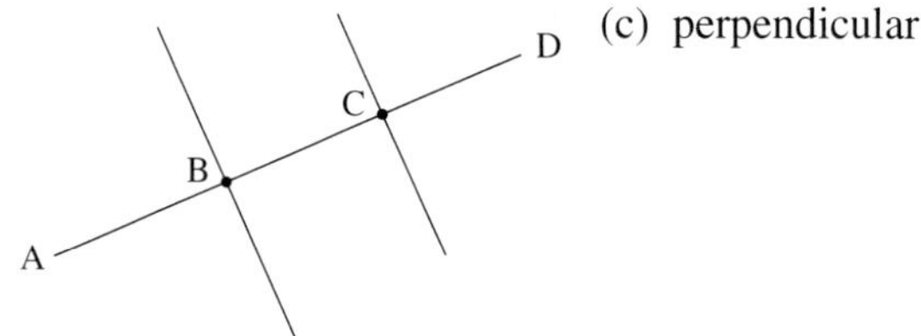

Page 76 ***HWK 2M/2E***

1. D **2.** scalene **3.** A **4.** **5.** C, F **7.** square, rectangle **8.** 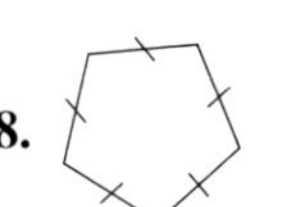 **9.** 4

4.3 Percentages

Page 77 ***HWK 1M***

1. (a) $\frac{48}{100} = \frac{12}{25}$ (b) $\frac{15}{100} = 15\%$ (c) $\frac{37}{100} = 37\%$ (d) $\frac{4}{10} = \frac{40}{100} = 40\%$ (e) $\frac{16}{100} = 0.16$

(f) $\frac{67}{100} = 0.67$ **2.** (a) $\frac{3}{5}$ (b) $\frac{6}{25}$ (c) $\frac{59}{100}$ (d) $\frac{7}{20}$ (e) $\frac{16}{25}$

3. (a) 0.49 (b) 0.4 (c) 0.08 (d) 0.13 (e) 0.85 **4.** 45%

5. (a) $\frac{88}{200} = \frac{11}{25}$ (b) 56%

Page 78 ***HWK 1E***

1. $\frac{36}{100}, \frac{18}{50}, \frac{72}{200}$ **2.** 25% **3.** 9% **4.** $\frac{13}{20}$ **5.** (a) $\frac{1}{4}, \frac{3}{10}$, 0.4 (b) 38%, 0.39, $\frac{2}{5}$

(c) 69%, 0.7, $\frac{18}{25}$ **6.** $\frac{4}{25} = 0.16$, $95\% = \frac{19}{20}$, $0.75 = \frac{3}{4}$, $20\% = \frac{1}{5}$, $0.3 = 30\%$

Page 78 ***HWK 2M***

1. 80% **3.** 30% **4.** 60% **5.** 65% **6.** $\frac{1}{3}$

7. (a) 60% (b) 75% (c) 20% (d) 90%

Page 79 ***HWK 3M***

1. (a) £9 (b) £8 (c) £9 odd one out is (b) **2.** (a) £24 (b) £24 (c) £15 odd one out is (c)
3. 28 **4.** (a) £40 (b) 3 kg (c) £112 **5.** 108 **6.** B(£60), C(£64), A(£70) **7.** 84 mm

Page 80 ***HWK 3E***

1. 66.5 kg **2.** 40 cm **3.** 720 **4.** shirt, trousers **5.** Diane by £12 **6.** £6800

Page 80 ***HWK 4M***

1. (a) £49 (b) £360 (c) £7.80 (d) £5.85 **2.** (a) £32 (b) £224
3. (a) £477 (b) £112.80 (c) £273 **4.** £0.70 or 70 pence
5. (a) 83.6 km (b) 1241 g (c) 259.7 kg **6.** £1479744

Page 81 ***HWK 4E***

1. (a) £7208 (b) £515.20 (c) £627.80 (d) £443.30 **2.** 100.8 cm **3.** £36.80
4. (a) A (b) B (c) £2.38 **5.** 1.59 m **6.** 92.4 ml

4.4 Proportion and ratio

Page 81 ***HWK 1M***

1. £48 **2.** £1.61 **3.** £40 **4.** £11.70 **5.** £4500 **6.** £141
7. £4.16 **8.** 30 minutes **9.** 4 toilet rolls for £1.68 **10.** 8 onions for £1.12

Page 82 ***HWK 1E***

1. $\frac{40}{160} = \frac{1}{4}$ **2.** $\frac{21}{50}$ **3.** $\frac{4}{15}$ **4.** $\frac{7}{10}$ **5.** 260 euros **6.** 1880 dollars
7. (a) $\frac{1}{2}$ (b) $\frac{3}{8}$ **8.** 324

Page 83 ***HWK 2M***

1. 13:6 **2.** 26:17 **3.** 6:3 = 2:1 **4.** 6:4 = 3:2 **5.** 9 black squares
6. (a) 1:8 (b) 1:3 (c) 4:3 (d) 3:2 (e) 2:4:5 **7.** yes
8. (a) 3 (b) 2 (c) 8 (d) 9 (e) 3 (f) 4

Page 83 ***HWK 2E***

1. (a) £40:£20 (b) £42:£18 (c) £24:£36 **2.** (a) £12:£36 (b) £30:£18 (c) £8:£40
3. Sid 8, Aisha 16 **4.** £105:£30 **5.** 35 **6.** £30 **7.** blue 18, red 3, yellow 15

4.5 Negative numbers

Page 84 ***HWK 1M***

1. (a) 8 (b) 5 (c) 7 **2.** –5°C **3.** (a) 4°C (b) –4°C

4. –3°C **5.** (a) –7°C, –4°C, –2°C, 1°C, 2°C, 6°C
(b) –8°C, –5°C, –3°C, –1°C, 0°C, 5°C

6. 9°C **7.** –£50 **8.** (a) false (b) false (c) false (d) true

Page 84 ***HWK 1E***

1. (a) –28 (b) –6 (c) –18 (d) –36 (e) –40 (f) –42
(g) –24 (h) –24 **2.** (a) –4 (b) –5 (c) –5 (d) –8
(e) 9 (f) 5 (g) –4 (h) 5 **3.** 6, –3, –18, 2, –9, –3, 3, –7, –21

4. (a) 25 (b) –48 (c) 24 (d) 16 (e) –84 (f) –8

5. –2, –3, 6, –5, –30, –2, 15, –3, –5

Page 85 ***HWK 2M***

1. (a) –4 (b) –1 (c) –3 (d) –2 (e) –5 (f) –3
(g) –7 (h) –2 **2.** (a) –6 (b) –4 (c) –8 (d) 7
(e) –7 (f) –2 (g) 0 (h) –10 **3.** 5–9, –6 + 2, –7 + 3, –2 – 2

4. (a) –3 (b) –3 (c) –4 (d) –5 (e) –2 (f) –4

5. 4

Page 85 ***HWK 2E***

1. (a) 10 (b) 2 (c) 12 (d) –5 (e) –6 (f) –1
(g) –2 (h) –9 **2.** (a) false (b) false (c) true (d) true
(e) false (f) true

3.

+	–4	2	–6	–3	1
–2	–6	0	–8	–5	–1
–3	–7	–1	–9	–6	–2
9	5	11	3	6	10
5	1	7	–1	2	6
–7	–11	–5	–13	–10	–6

4. –10

4.6 More algebra

Page 86 ***HWK 1M***

1. $m = 10$ **2.** $y = 10$ **3.** $p = 28$ **4.** $b = 81$ **5.** $a = 35$ **6.** $v = 52$
7. $y = 120$ **8.** $a = 7$ **9.** $m = 30$ **10.** $y = 28$ **11.** $A = 72$ **12.** $p = 66$

Page 87 ***HWK 1E***

1. $y = 32$ **2.** $m = 9$ **3.** $a = -36$ **4.** $y = -16$ **5.** $p = -31$ **6.** $c = -36$
7. $m = -6$ **8.** $a = 16$ **9.** $y = -66$ **10.** $m = -11$ **11.** $p = 54$ **12.** $a = -57$

Page 87 ***HWK 2M***

1. 6 **2.** 14 **3.** 13 **4.** 9 **5.** 8 **6.** 7
7. 3 **8.** 3 **9.** 6 **10.** 5 **11.** 7 **12.** 4

Page 88 ***HWK 3M***

1. 4 **2.** 11 **3.** 22 **4.** 4 **5.** 15 **6.** 22
7. 6 **8.** 5 **9.** 8 **10.** 0 **11.** 36 **12.** 42
13. 40 **14.** 48 **15.** 36 **16.** 7 **17.** 10 **18.** 12
19. 48 **20.** 26 **21.** 12 **22.** 49 **23.** 0 **24.** 45
25. 0.5 **26.** 3 **27.** 431

Page 88 ***HWK 3E***

1. 3 **2.** 7 **3.** 8 **4.** 10 **5.** 5 **6.** 1
7. 9 **8.** 4 **9.** 20 **10.** 2 **11.** 15 **12.** 25
13. 6 **14.** 8 **15.** 50 **16.** 4 **17.** 0 **18.** 7
19. 10 **20.** 3 **21.** 100 **22.** 2 **23.** 30 **24.** 9

Page 89 ***HWK 4M***

1. 6 **2.** 8 **3.** 25 **4.** 7 **5.** 9 **6.** 6
7. 20 **8.** 5

Page 89 ***HWK 4E***

1. $x = 7$ **2.** $x = 8$ **3.** $x = 3$ **4.** $x = 10$ **5.** $x = 15$ **6.** $x = 2$
7. $x = 17$ **8.** $x = 7$ **9.** $x = 0$ **10.** $x = 32$ **11.** $x = 18$ **12.** $x = 12$
13. $m = 6$ **14.** $w = 120$ **15.** $y = 13$ **16.** $a = 250$ **17.** $p = 35$ **18.** $n = 8$
19. $b = 130$ **20.** $x = 45$ **21.** $q = 195$

Page 90 ***HWK 5M***

1. $5x + 20$ **2.** $3a + 27$ **3.** $2b - 14$ **4.** $6m - 18$ **5.** $8y + 32$ **6.** $24 + 4n$
7. $6m + 6n$ **8.** $6x - 12$ **9.** $15p + 25$ **10.** $32y - 40$ **11.** $12a + 18$ **12.** $2x - 2y$
13. $36 - 9q$ **14.** $6a + 15b$ **15.** $18m + 6$ **16.** $21c + 14d$ **17.** $40w - 35$ **18.** $8a + 4b + 20$
19. $18m - 81n$ **20.** $28p + 32q$ **21.** $24 + 9y - 21x$

Page 90 ***HWK 5E***

1. $ab + ad$ **2.** $my - mw$ **3.** $np + 4n$ **4.** $pq - 5p$ **5.** $cd - 8c$ **6.** $xy + 3x$
7. $5b + \mathrm{bc}$ **8.** $n^2 + 7n$ **9.** $a^2 - 6a$ **10.** $3p + pw$ **11.** $9x - x^2$ **12.** $12n + 8$
13. $56a - 28$ **14.** $m^2 - 2m$ **15.** $15q - 45$ **16.** $9y + y^2$ **17.** $4b - bc$ **18.** $24w + 21$
19. $12 + 24m$ **20.** $x^2 - 4x$ **21.** $7a - a^2$

UNIT 5

5.1 Rotation

Page 91 ***HWK 1M***

1. 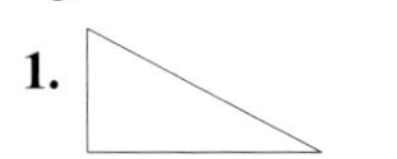 **2.**  **3.** 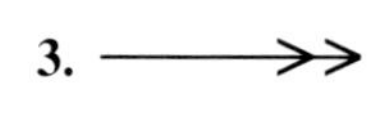 **4.** 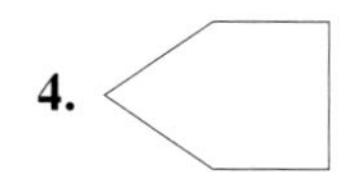 **5.** 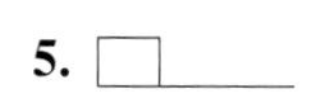 **6.** 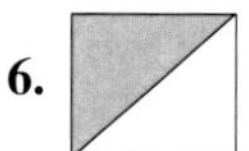

7. 90° anti-clockwise **8.** 180° clockwise **9.** 90° clockwise **10.** 90° clockwise

11. 90° anti-clockwise **12.** 90° clockwise

Page 92 ***HWK 1E***

1.

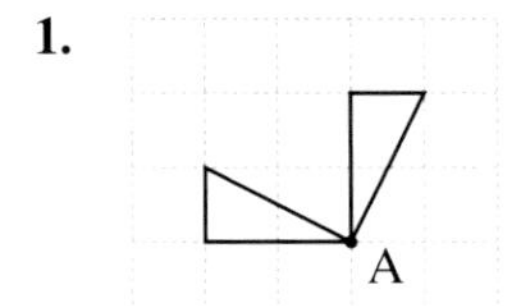

2.

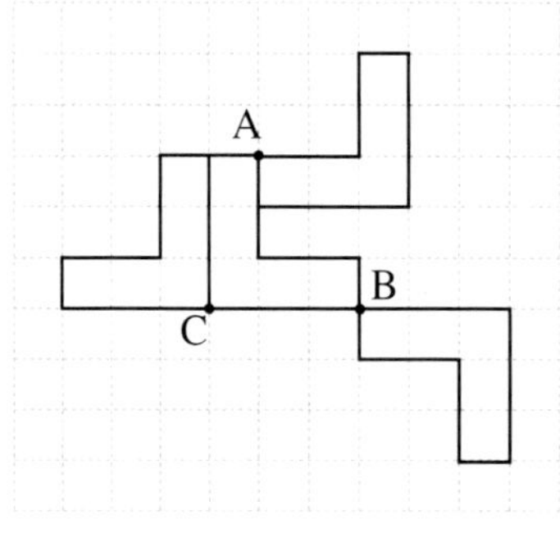

3.

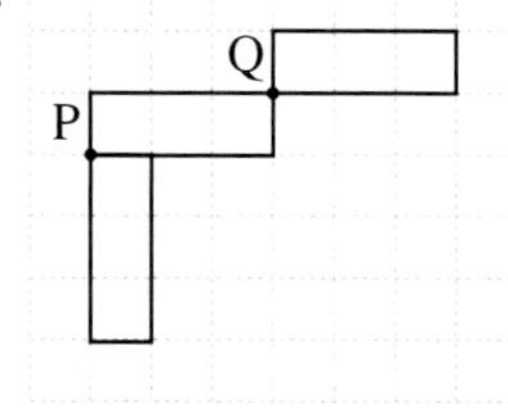

4. (a) P (b) Q (c) M (d) P

Page 93 ***HWK 2M/2E***

1. (a) yes, 2 (b) yes, 6 (c) yes, 2 (d) none (e) yes, 8 (f) none
(g) yes, 5 (h) yes, 2

2. (a)

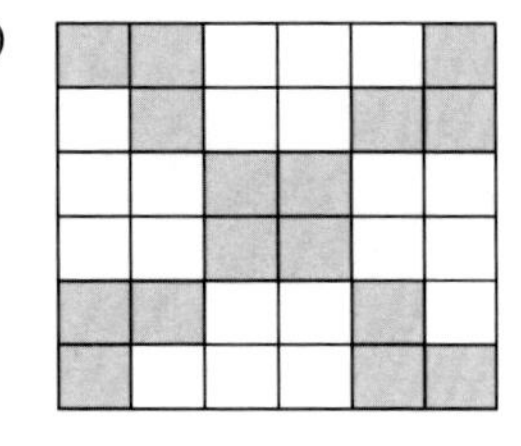

(b)

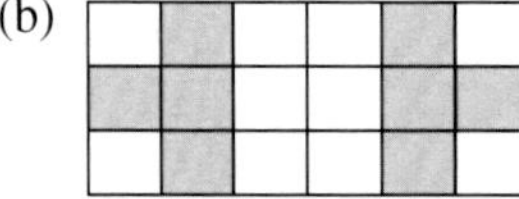

(c)

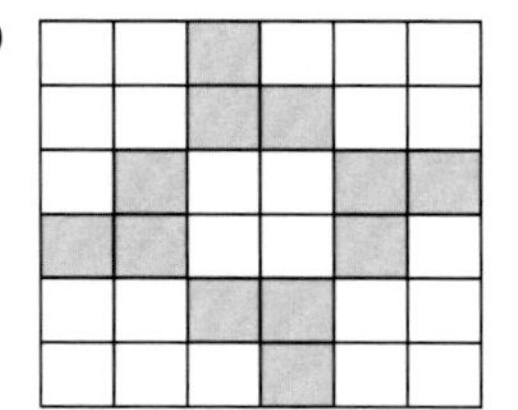

5.2 Line symmetry

Page 93 ***HWK 1M***

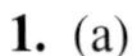

1. (a)

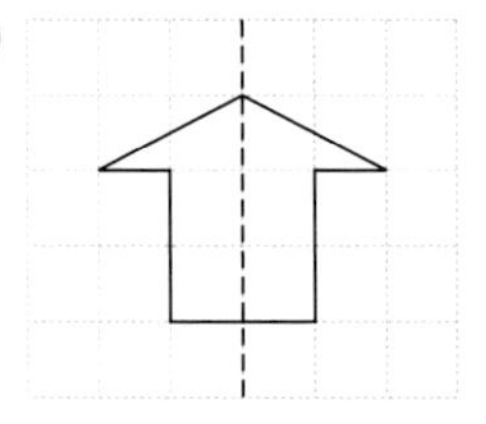

(b)

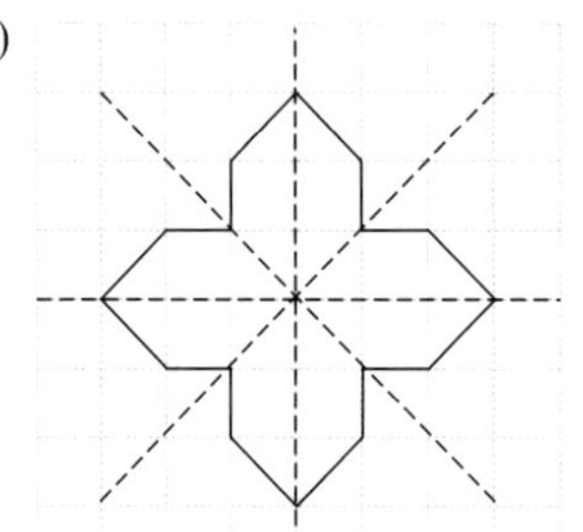

(c)

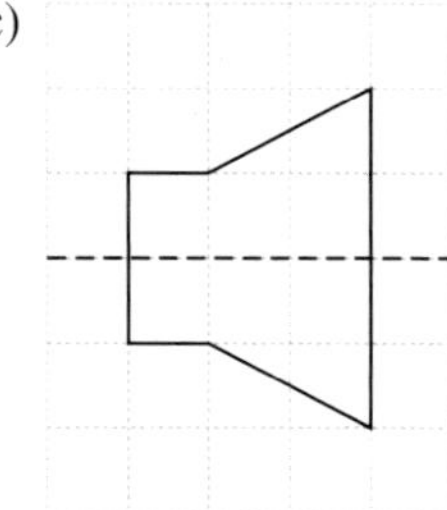

(d)

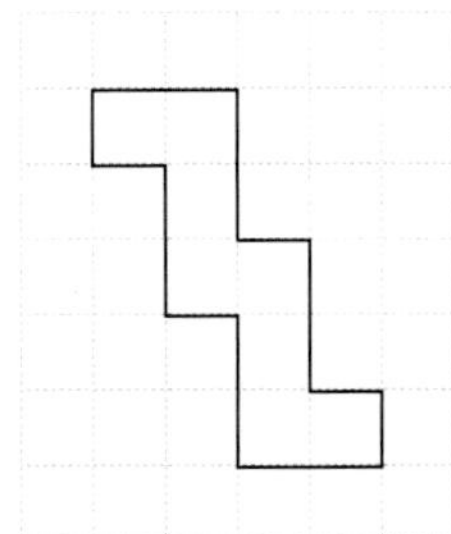

(e)

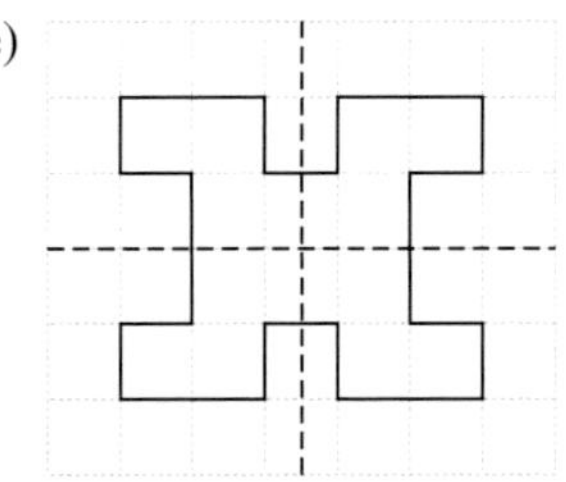

(f)

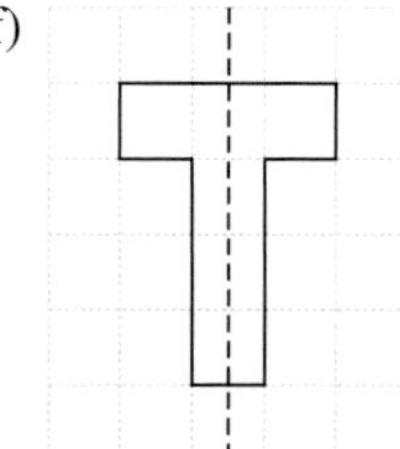

Page 94 ***HWK 1E***

1. (a) S (b) S **2.** 8 **3.** (a)

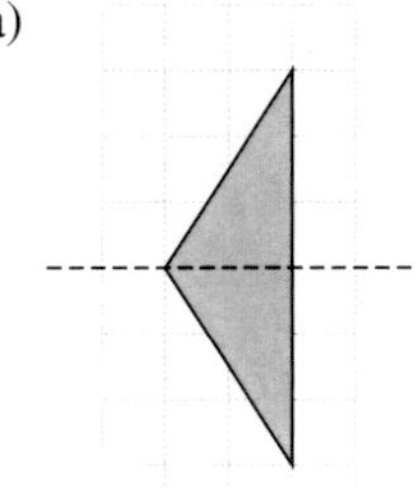

(b)

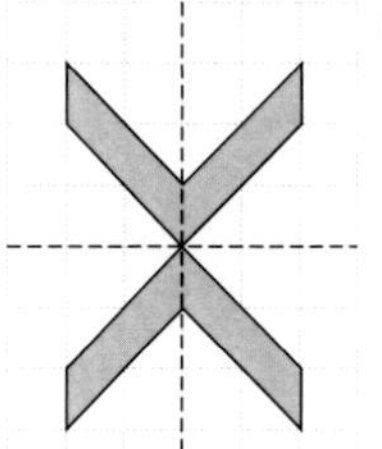

(c)

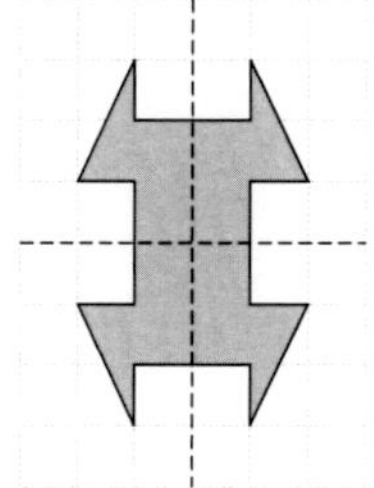

4. (a) yes, 2 (b) yes, order 2

Page 95 ***HWK 2M/2E***

1.

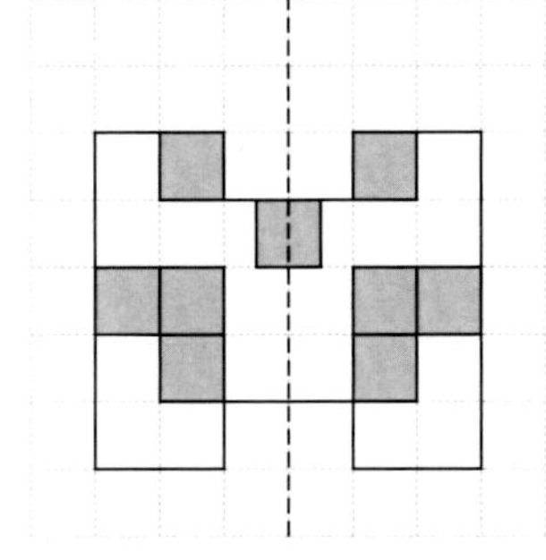

4 new squares

2.

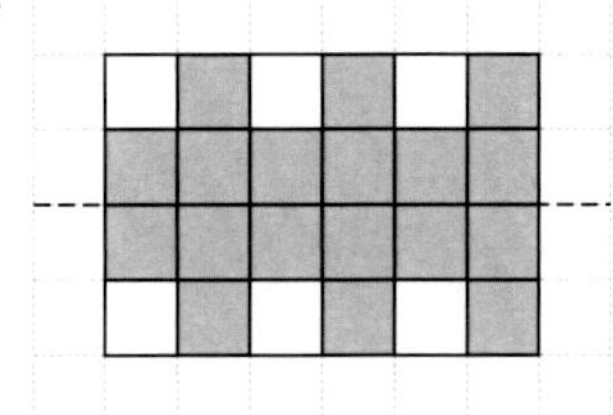

9 new squares

3.

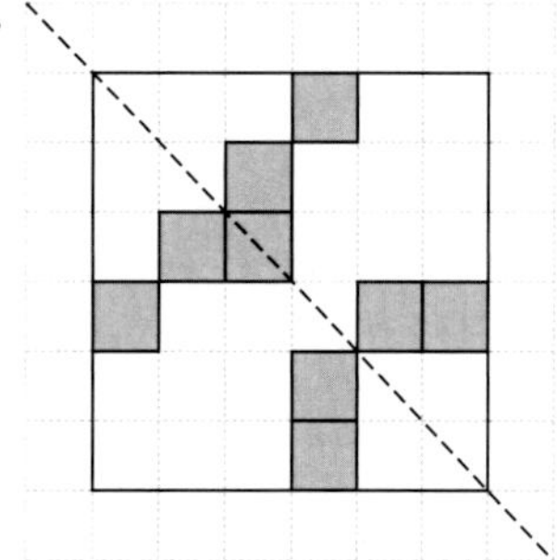

4 new squares

4.

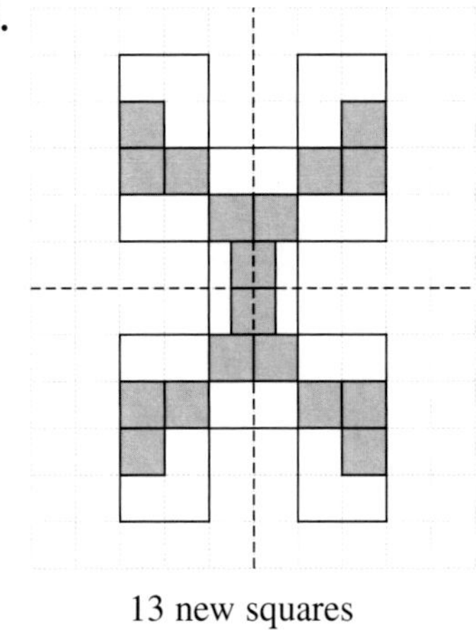

13 new squares

5.

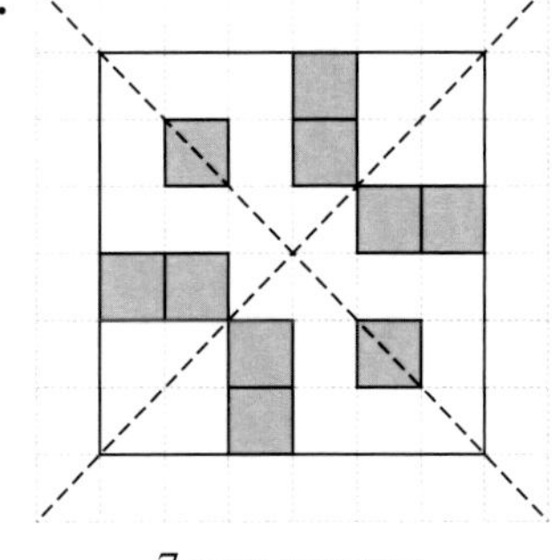

7 new squares

6.

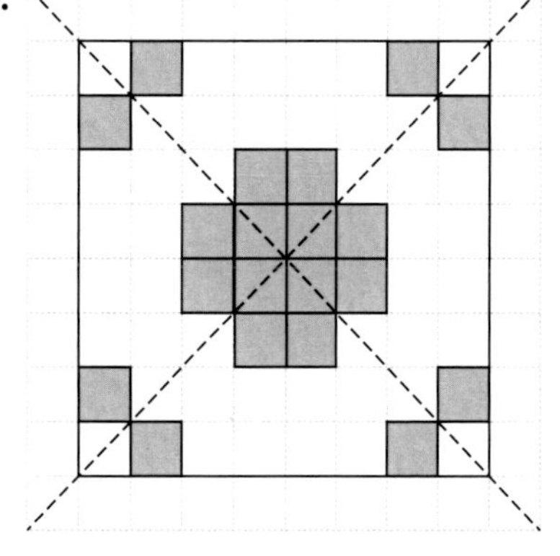

17 new squares

5.3 Translation

Page 96 ***HWK 1M***

1.

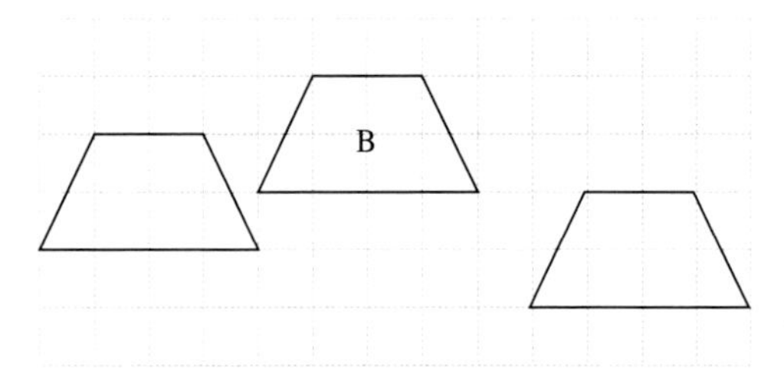

2.e

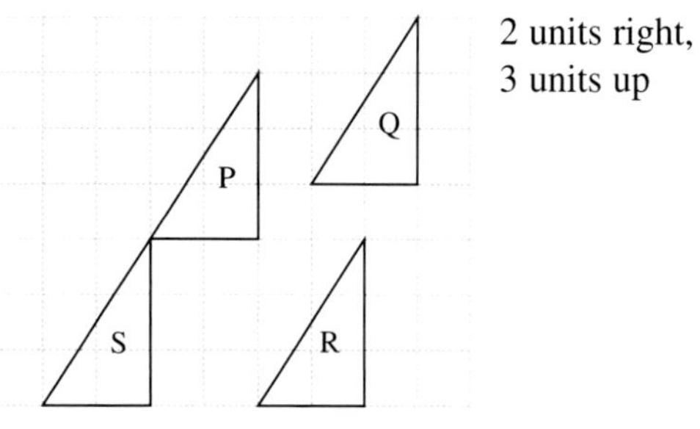

2 units right, 3 units up

3. (a) 2 units right, 4 units down (b) 3 units down (c) 2 units left, 2 units down
(d) 4 units left, 5 units up

Page 97 ***HWK 1E***

1. (a) 1 right, 3 down (b) 4 right (c) 4 left, 2 up (d) 1 right, 2 down (e) 2 down (f) 1 left, 4 up

2. (a) T (b) T (c) Q (d) U

3.

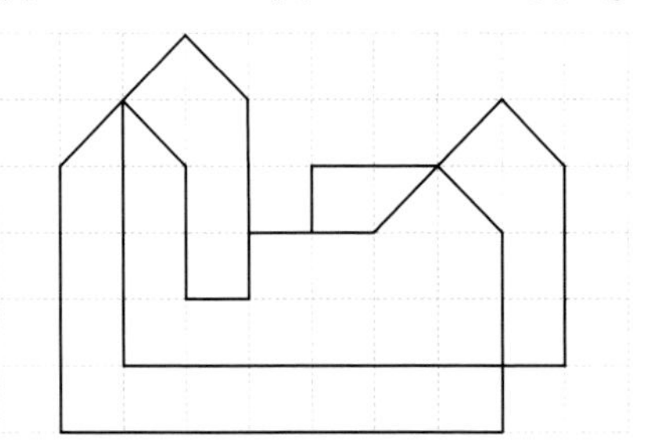

5.4 Number review

Page 97 ***HWK 1M***

1. (a) true (b) false (c) false (d) true

2. (a) 1, 2, [4], 8 (b) 1, 2, 4, 5, [10], [20] (c) 1, 2, [3], 5, [6], [10], [15], 30

3. 5, 10, 15, 20, 25, 30 **4.** 11, 13, 17, 19 **5.** (a) 30 (b) 16

6. No. Divisible by 3 or 13 **7.** 1, 2, 3, 4, 6, 8, 12, 16, 24, 48

Page 98 ***HWK 1E***

1. (a) 4, 8, 12, 16, 20 (b) 6, 12, 18, 24, 30, (c) 12

2. (a) 40 (b) 28 (c) 24 **3.** 53

4. (a) 1, 2, 4, 5, 8, 10, 20, 40 (b) 1, 2, 5, 10, 25, 50 (c) 10

5. (a) 5 (b) 4 (c) 5 **6.** 4 has three factors, the others have two factors only.

Page 98 ***HWK 2M***

1. $\frac{10}{16}$ **2.** (a) $\frac{2}{5}$ (b) $\frac{7}{10}$ (c) $\frac{1}{4}$ (d) $\frac{5}{6}$ (e) $\frac{3}{8}$ (f) $\frac{2}{5}$

3. (a) true (b) false (c) true **4.** (a) 5% (b) $\frac{40}{100} = 40\%$

(c) $\frac{36}{100} = 36\%$ **5.** (a) $\frac{32}{100} = 0.32$ (b) $\frac{9}{100} = 0.09$ (c) $\frac{1}{4} = 0.25$

6. (a) $\frac{6}{7}$ (b) $\frac{3}{5}$ (c) $\frac{5}{6}$ (d) $\frac{3}{8}$

Page 99 ***HWK 2E***

1. (a) $\frac{2}{5}$ (b) $\frac{1}{4}$ (c) $\frac{9}{20}$ (d) $\frac{2}{25}$ (e) $\frac{23}{50}$

2. (a) 7% (b) 32% (c) 50% (d) 60% (e) 16%

3. (a) $\frac{3}{5}$ (b) $\frac{19}{100}$ (c) $\frac{7}{20}$ (d) $\frac{8}{25}$ (e) $\frac{1}{50}$

4. 0.303 **5.** 1.4 **6.** Yes by 3% **7.** (a) $\frac{2}{5}$, 0.42, 45%

(b) $\frac{1}{20}$, 10%, 0.2 (c) 0.68, $\frac{7}{10}$, 73%

Page 99 ***HWK 3M***

1. 480 **2.** 336 **3.** 792 **4.** 2322 **5.** 22

6. 33 **7.** 24 **8.** 3159 **9.** 16 **10.** 38

11. 8704 **12.** 13 **13.** (a) 468 (b) 27 (c) 32

Page 100 ***HWK 3E***

1. 53 **2.** 5 **3.** £ 1696 **4.** 12 days **5.** £19 **6.** 612

Page 100 ***HWK 4M***

1. (a) 18.8 (b) 14.6 (c) 3.72 (d) 0.556 **2.** £2.26

3. (a) 8.6 (b) 0.39 (c) 2.83 (d) 27.6 **4.** 4 – 2.1

5. 0.37 kg **6.** 3.86, 4.4, 8.26, 6, 2.26 **7.** (a) 3.65 + 3.73 = 7.38

(b) 2.96 + 5.38 = 8.34 (c) 8.07 – 2.64 = 5.43

Page 101 ***HWK 4E***

1. (a) false (b) true (c) true (d) true (e) false (f) true

2. £0.28 **3.** £5.60 **4.** (a) 36.72 (b) 1.44 (c) 1.56 (d) 4.3

(e) 7.77 (f) 4.3 (g) 18.96 (h) 2.16 **5.** 60.2 g

6. 6, 1.48, 8.88, 3, 2.96

Page 101 ***HWK 5M***

1. (a) 30 g (b) 30 kg (c) £24 (d) 9 m (e) 12 cm (f) 7 g

(g) 8 m (h) £21 **2.** $\frac{1}{3}$ of £21 **3.** (a) 4 (b) 12 (c) 4

(d) 20 (e) 36 (f) 6 (g) 14 (h) 72 **4.** $\frac{3}{5}$ of 60

5. 228 **6.** (a) 10% (b) 20% (c) $\frac{1}{6}$ (d) $\frac{1}{3}$ (e) 18 (f) 120

Page 102 ***HWK 5E***

1. (a) £37.80 (b) 408 g (c) £94.80 **2.** 6640 **3.** 8% of £68 by £0.04

4. (a) 6% (b) $66\frac{2}{3}$% (c) 75% (d) 55% **5.** $\frac{1}{3}$ of £1773

6. £1098 **7.** £18.27

5.5 Probability 2

Page 102 ***HWK 1M***

1. (a) $\frac{1}{3}$ (b) $\frac{1}{3}$ **2.** (a) $\frac{3}{5}$ (b) $\frac{2}{5}$ **3.** $\frac{3}{12} = \frac{1}{4}$

4. (a) $\frac{1}{6}$ (b) $\frac{2}{6} = \frac{1}{3}$ **5.** (a) $\frac{3}{7}$ (b) $\frac{4}{7}$ (c) $\frac{1}{7}$

Page 103 ***HWK 1E***

1. (a) $\frac{7}{18}$ (b) $\frac{3}{18} = \frac{1}{6}$ (c) 0 **2.** (a) $\frac{2}{7}$ (b) $\frac{1}{7}$ (c) $\frac{2}{7}$ **3.** $\frac{1}{16}$

4. odd number **5.** (a) $\frac{2}{10} = \frac{1}{5}$ (b) $\frac{3}{10}$ (c) $\frac{3}{10}$ (d) $\frac{6}{10} = \frac{3}{5}$

Page 104 ***HWK 2M***

1. (a) $\frac{4}{11}$ (b) $\frac{2}{11}$ (c) $\frac{5}{11}$ (d) $\frac{2}{11}$ **2.** (a) $\frac{1}{52}$ (b) $\frac{4}{52} = \frac{1}{13}$

(c) $\frac{26}{52} = \frac{1}{2}$ (d) $\frac{13}{52} = \frac{1}{4}$ **3.** $\frac{5}{6}$ **4.** (a) $\frac{7}{10}$ (b) pink **5.** (a) $\frac{4}{16} = \frac{1}{4}$

(b) $\frac{2}{16} = \frac{1}{8}$ (c) $\frac{1}{16}$

Page 104 ***HWK 2E***

1. $\frac{1}{4}$ **2.** (a) $\frac{1}{6}$ (b) $\frac{4}{6} = \frac{2}{3}$ (c) $\frac{2}{6} = \frac{1}{3}$ **3.** 4

4. (a) (H, H) (H, T) (T, H) (T, T) (b) $\frac{1}{4}$ (c) $\frac{1}{4}$ **5.** (a) $\frac{14}{18} = \frac{7}{9}$ (b) $\frac{5}{21}$

5.6 Interpreting graphs

Page 105 ***HWK 1M/1E***

1. (a) (i) 30 (ii) 30 (iii) 5 (b) 09.00 (c) 10.00 and 18.00

(d) 30 minutes **2.** (a) (i) 4 inches (ii) 8 inches (iii) 2 inches (b) 7 inches

3. (a) 10 cm (b) 35 cm (c) after 3 minutes (d) 1 minute 15 secs

(e) let some water out by removing the plug (f) 45 seconds

Page 107 ***HWK 2M***

1. (a) 2.7 litres (b) 1.4 gallons **2.** (b) $3\frac{1}{2}$ minutes (c) 67.5 kcals

Page 107 ***HWK 2E***

1. (a) 40 miles (b) 45 minutes (c) 25 miles (d) 50 mph

(e) 45 minutes **2.** (a) 30 minutes (b) 3.45 p.m. (c) 3

(d) 15 km/h **3.** (a) 08.45 (b) 50 km (c) 85 km (d) 50 km/h

5.7 Algebra Review

Page 109 ***HWK 1M***

1. 12 **2.** 24 **3.** 24 **4.** 5 **5.** 74 **6.** 2
7. 25 **8.** 64 **9.** 36 **10.** 4 **11.** $3m + 7n$ **12.** $5y + 2w$
13. $f + 4g$ **14.** $12a + 3$ **15.** $5x + 3y$ **16.** $2p + q + 4$ **17.** b **18.** false
19. $y \times 3, y + 2y, 4y - y$ **20.** $b + 5a + b, 4a + 3b + a - b$

Page 109 ***HWK 1E***

1. –6 **2.** 0 **3.** –15 **4.** –11 **5.** –12
6. 9 **7.** –3 **8.** 30 **9.** –18 **10.** 0
11. $h = 25$ **12.** $a = 16$ **13.** $m = -32$ **14.** $w = 42$ **15.** $y = 27$
16. $b = -56$ **17.** $a = -24$ **18.** $m = 25$ **19.** $q = -9$ **20.** $y = -4$

5.8 Rounding numbers

Page 110 ***HWK 1M***

1. (a) 30 (b) 50 (c) 80 (d) 130 (e) 80 (f) 310
2. (a) 400 (b) 400 (c) 800 (d) 1600 (e) 1700 (f) 41400
3. 13.7, 13.5, 14.16, 14.4 **4.** (a) 3000 (b) 5000 (c) 1000 (d) 12000
(e) 30000 (f) 315000 **5.** (a) true (b) true (c) false (d) true

Page 110 ***HWK 1E***

1. (a) 1800 (b) 280 (c) 92000 (d) 317000 (e) 2600 (f) 18
2. (a) 260 (b) 1730 (c) 70 (d) 460 (e) 70 (f) 2770
3. 23712, 23673, 23689 **4.** (a) 35 (b) 8 (c) 61 (d) 3
(e) 86 (f) 25 (g) 16 (h) 5

Page 111 ***HWK 2M/2E***

1. (a) 3.8 (b) 7.9 (c) 23.5 (d) 3.7 (e) 8.6 (f) 8.0
(g) 38.7 (h) 24.3 (i) 4.3 (j) 2.6 **2.** 34.428, 34.35, 34.38, 34.439
3. (a) 5.4 cm by 2.8 cm (b) 15.1 cm^2 **4.** (a) 23.4 (b) 1.3 (c) 1.1
(d) 7.8 (e) 4.3 (f) 1.9 (g) 3.4 (h) 399.2

Page 112 ***HWK 3M***

1. A **2.** C **3.** C **4.** A **5.** B **6.** A
7. A **8.** B **9.** C **10.** C **11.** B **12.** A

Page 112 ***HWK 3E***

1. £180 **2.** (a) £45 (b) £45.75 **3.** £9600 **4.** 18 cm^2 **5.** £16.50
6. 12.1×19.78 **7.** 40 cm

Unit 6

6.1 More equations

Page 114 ***HWK 1M***

1. (a) $n = 5$ (b) $x = 21$ (c) $y = 12$ (d) $p = 15$ (e) $m = 8$
(f) $a = 15$ **2.** (a) $n = 7$ (b) $p = 3$ (c) $y = 10$ (d) $x = 8$
(e) $x = 4$ (f) $w = 9$ **3.** 11 **4.** 25 pence **5.** (a) $m = 4$
(b) $y = 20$ (c) $w = 7$ (d) $x = 15$ (e) $p = 30$ (f) $n = 6$

Page 114 ***HWK 1E***

1. (a) $n = \frac{3}{5}$ (b) $w = \frac{2}{7}$ (c) $\frac{1}{8} = p$ **2.** (a) $x = \frac{1}{3}$ (b) $y = \frac{2}{5}$ (c) $m = \frac{5}{6}$
(d) $y = \frac{3}{4}$ (e) $m = \frac{7}{10}$ (f) $p = \frac{8}{9}$ **3.** $\frac{3}{8}$ **4.** (a) $n = \frac{6}{7}$ (b) $x = \frac{1}{4}$
(c) $p = \frac{4}{5}$ (d) $y = \frac{5}{8}$ (e) $w = \frac{1}{7}$ (f) $m = \frac{13}{15}$

6.2 Sequence rules

Page 115 ***HWK 1M***

1. (b) 4 times the shape number and then add 1.
2. (c) 4 times the shape number and then add 4.
3. (b) 9, 16, 23, 30 (c) 7 times the shape number and then add 2.

Page 116 ***HWK 2M***

1. (a) 10 (b) 19 (c) 157 (d) 3007 **2.** 2, 6, 10, 14, 18 **3.** $2n + 1$
4. 7, 13, 19, 25, 31 **5.** $4n + 3$ **6.** (a) $3n$ (b) $7n$ (c) $3n + 2$ (d) $9n - 4$

6.3 Metric and imperial units

Page 116 ***HWK 1M***

1. (a) 7000 g (b) 900 cm (c) 350 cm (d) 4 kg (e) 6 cm (f) 2600 m
(g) 7500 ml (h) 0.2 kg (i) 0.3 m (j) 9400 m (k) 8.5 kg (l) 46 mm
(m) 8 litres (n) 0.5 m (o) 400 g (p) 0.35 km **2.** 1700 ml or 1.7 litres
3. 800 m **4.** 4 **5.** 170 cm or 1.7 m.

Page 117 ***HWK 1E***

1. (a) 22 pounds (b) 20 gallons (c) 48 km (d) 3 kg (e) 27 litres
(f) 240 cm (g) 20 kg (h) 20 miles (i) 13.2 pounds **2.** 100 miles
3. Tania by 2 cm **4.** bag by 0.1 pound **5.** 1.5 litres **6.** 500 g

Page 117 ***HWK 2M***

1. $a = 4, b = 3.5, c = 1.5$ **2.** $a = 850, b = 700, c = 600$ **3.** 25 **4.** 7.5